Achilles

GOLDEN TALES OF GREECE

Achilles

Retold by Compton Mackenzie
Illustrated by William Stobbs

WORLD PUBLISHING
TIMES MIRROR
NEW YORK

GODS AND GODDESSES

IN THE STORY OF ACHILLES

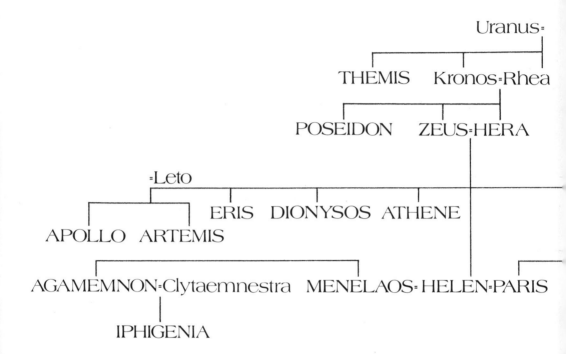

First U.S. edition published 1972 by The World Publishing Company,
110 East 59th Street, New York City, New York
Published simultaneously in Canada by Nelson, Foster & Scott Ltd.
Copyright © 1972 by Aldus Books Limited, London
All rights reserved
Library of Congress catalog card number: 72-8686
ISBN: 0-529-04730-6
Printed and bound in Yugoslavia by Mladinska Knjiga, Ljubljana

WORLD PUBLISHING
TIMES MIRROR

Gaea=Pontus
|
Nereus=Doris
|
THETIS=PELEUS
|
ACHILLES

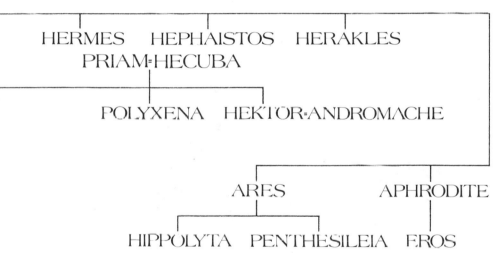

HERMES   HEPHAISTOS   HERAKLES
PRIAM=HECUBA

POLYXENA   HEKTOR=ANDROMACHE

ARES   APHRODITE

HIPPOLYTA   PENTHESILEIA   EROS

This family tree shows the gods and goddesses of ancient Greece, and the demi-gods and mortals related to them, whose lives are linked with that of Achilles, the hero of this story of once upon a time. Those whose names are in capitals—for example, ATHENE and PARIS—played a direct part in Achilles' adventures. Those whose names are not in capitals—such as Leto, mother of APOLLO—take their places in the tree as links in the line of descent from Gaea, the Earth-mother. It was believed in that world of long ago that Gaea was created out of Chaos. She brought forth Uranus (Heaven) and Pontus (Sea), by both of whom she then had children. From her were descended all the other gods and goddesses of Greece.

Achilles

Once upon a time there was a beautiful sea-nymph called Thetis, who was one of the Nereids, the daughters of a minor sea-god called Nereus. Zeus, the father of gods and men, and Poseidon, his brother and god of the sea, were rivals for her hand. But Thetis refused to marry either. Zeus she refused out of love and gratitude to his wife Hera, who had brought her up. Poseidon she refused because she felt that the other Nereids would be jealous if the great god of the sea set her above them as queen.

Both Zeus and Poseidon were disappointed by their failure to win Thetis. But their disappointment turned to relief when Themis, the goddess of law and order, told them the Fates had prophesied that any son of Thetis would grow up to be greater than his father. They agreed that they had had a lucky escape and decided that, to avoid trouble to the gods, Thetis must marry a mortal.

Their choice fell upon Peleus, a mighty hunter and warrior who was much loved by the gods. Peleus was one of the Heroes who had been brought up by the centaur Cheiron in his cave on Mount Pelion. One of Peleus's companions on Pelion had been Jason, and Peleus had been one of the first to answer Jason's appeal for volunteers to sail in the *Argo* to bring back the Golden Fleece to

A beautiful sea-nymph called Thetis

Hellas. Peleus happened to be visiting his old tutor on Mount Pelion when the decision was taken that he was to be the mortal husband of one of the immortal Nereids. Cheiron broke the news to him.

"But you will be wise, my son, to win Thetis's love. She has a strong mind of her own, and I do not think even the great Zeus himself could force her to marry you against her will."

"What shall I do to win her love?" Peleus asked.

"There is a tiny islet close to the shore at the foot of Pelion. On this islet is a small cave whose entrance is almost hidden by a bush of myrtle. It is Thetis's habit to rest in that cave after bathing. You must hide in the cave, and when she comes in you must take her in your arms. She will resist you and turn herself into all kinds of dangerous shapes to make you let go of her. But, if you can stand the pain you will suffer, she will yield at last."

So Peleus went down to the shore and swam out to the islet. Here he hid himself in the cave and waited. And then over the wine-dark sea came a bridled dolphin on whose back the lovely Nereid was riding. Peleus watched her bathing, fascinated by her grace and beauty. When at last she walked to the cave to rest, he sprang out from behind his hiding place and held her tightly. Thetis instantly turned herself into fire and burned him; then she turned into a cuttlefish and squirted ink all over him; then she became a lion that tore him with its claws; then she became a serpent and struck at him with her fangs.

In spite of being burned and blistered, blinded, mauled, and stung, Peleus did not loosen his hold. Finally Thetis surrendered, and they passionately embraced.

The wedding ceremony and feast was timed for the full moon, and the twelve gods of Olympus decided to attend the wedding. Hera was responsible for this decision. Nowhere in all the rich mythology of Greece is there any other instance of the gods attending a mortal wedding. Hera sent Iris, her rainbow-winged messenger, to invite all the older gods as well as the twelve Olympians. Unfortunately, one of the older immortals—Eris, the ugly goddess of strife—was overlooked. However, she attended the wedding uninvited and, just as the guests were about to drink to the bride and bridegroom, she rolled a golden apple into the assembly.

Peleus quickly picked it up. Then he saw that it carried an inscription. It read: *To the Fairest.*

Zeus saw that Hera, Aphrodite, and Athene were waiting expectantly for Peleus to present the golden apple to one of them.

"Give the apple to me," Zeus commanded.

And the embarrassed Peleus gratefully obeyed.

The golden apple would one day be known as the Apple of Discord, but at the time the interruption it caused was soon forgotten. The nine Muses began to sing an epithalamium, or wedding song. On the white beach below Mount Pelion, the Nereids danced as lightly as the wavelets themselves.

Thetis turned herself into fire

The Olympians' wedding gift to Peleus was a suit of golden armor. Poseidon gave him two of his immortal horses. Athene's gift was a spear whose blade had been forged by Hephaistos, god of fire and forger of metals.

After the marriage, Zeus ordered Peleus to capture Iolkos, the town in Thessaly from which the Argonauts had sailed. Zeus turned a swarm of ants, or Myrmidons, into an army, and with them Peleus afterward reigned in Iolkos as King of the Myrmidons.

In the course of time, the son who was to be greater than his sire was born to Thetis. He was named Achilles. Although he was born mortal, because he had a mortal father, Thetis longed for him to be immortal like herself. So she took the baby and dipped him into the Styx, the river of the Underworld. Achilles had now only one vulnerable spot—his right heel, by which his mother held him when she immersed him in the river.

At about this same time, in another country, there was born another baby boy, who was to play a decisive role in the future of Achilles. He was the son of King Priam and Queen Hecuba of Troy, that mighty city on the Asiatic side of the Hellespont. His name was Paris. A few days before he was born, his mother had dreamed that she had brought forth a firebrand from which issued innumerable flames in the shape of snakes. She had awakened from her nightmare screaming that the city of Troy and the forests of Mount Ida were burning. Priam, worried by the dream, consulted one of his seers who told him that the dream was a warning; the child Queen Hecuba was carrying would one day bring ruin to mighty Troy. King Priam then consulted a priest of Apollo, who confirmed the seer's interpretation and advised Priam to order the midwives to strangle the infant at birth. But, when Paris was born, Priam ordered Hecuba herself to kill him. Naturally, she refused. Then Priam ordered his herdsman Agelaos to kill the baby.

Agelaos could not bring himself to strangle or stab the infant. Instead, he took it to Mount Ida and left it there to die of exposure. Five days later he went back to assure himself that the baby was dead, so that he could tell his master that his orders had been carried out. But, to his amazement, he found the baby alive, being suckled by a she-bear. He could harden his heart no longer. He picked up the baby boy and carried him to his own home to be brought up with his own children.

Achilles, too, had an unusual infancy. When he was two years old, Thetis had a presentiment that he would lose his life in battle when he was only a young man. So, to save him from this fate, she proposed to have him brought up as a girl. Peleus, naturally, opposed this, and so Thetis left him and went back to live in her grotto under the sea. Peleus thereupon took his small son up to the cave on Mount Pelion to be brought up by the centaur Cheiron.

The young Achilles, fed by Cheiron on honey and the bone-marrow of fawns, learned to run faster than any of his age in all Hellas. He became so strong that, it is said, he

Achilles was dipped into the Styx

killed his first boar when he was six years old. Cheiron encouraged his athletic powers, but took care to train his mind as well as his body. The Muse Kalliope taught him music and song; Cheiron himself taught him medicine.

And now came tragedy. In the course of his Fourth Labor, the hunting of the Erymanthian boar, the mighty Herakles visited Mount Pelion and enjoyed Cheiron's hospitality. Young Achilles was proud to be presented to Herakles, who was already famous all over Hellas. But one day Cheiron was accidentally wounded in the knee by one of the deadly poisoned arrows of Herakles. In his agony he besought Almighty Zeus to take from him his immortality, so that death might end his suffering. Zeus granted the request and took Cheiron up into the heavens as the constellation Sagittarius.

After the death of Cheiron, Thetis reclaimed her son and took him to live with her on the island of Skyros. Here Achilles was brought up as a girl at the court of King Lykomedes, and here he stayed until he was about fifteen, when Peleus decided that he would no longer permit his only son to be brought up in this way.

"Zeus is planning a mighty war, with many woes for Hellas," argued Thetis. "I do not want my beloved son to be killed in battle while he is still young."

"But you made him invulnerable by dipping him into the Styx," Peleus retorted.

"Almost invulnerable," Thetis murmured sadly, remembering that unprotected heel.

However, Peleus was firm. He insisted that Achilles must have a male tutor. Unwillingly, Thetis agreed.

The tutor Peleus chose for Achilles was a distant kinsman called Phoinix, who had taken refuge with Peleus after his father had blinded him in a jealous rage. Peleus had taken Phoinix to Cheiron, who had restored his sight. Since then Phoinix had remained in Iolkos.

Achilles became very fond of his new tutor, and at the same time he started a devoted friendship with a youth a year or two older than himself whose name was Patrokles.

Away on Mount Ida the young Paris had kept pace with Achilles' athletic ability. He astonished the other herdsmen by his strength and skill and his handsome countenance and perfect figure.

Paris fell in love with a nymph called Oenone, who passionately returned his love. She used to accompany him on his hunting expeditions and applaud his handling of the herds. One of Paris's diversions was to set the bulls in Agelaos's herd against one another, crowning the victor with flowers and the loser with straw. Soon one of the bulls in the herd established his supremacy over all the others. Paris challenged the other herdsmen on Mount Ida to produce a bull that could defeat his champion. None could do so. Now Paris offered to pit his bull against any in Phrygia or Lydia, and promised to put a golden crown on the horns of the victor.

Ares, the god of war, told the other Olympians that for a joke he was going to turn himself into a bull and

The bull was crowned with flowers

fight Paris's champion. He invited them to watch the contest from Olympus. When Ares won, and Paris immediately and without argument crowned his horns with gold, the Olympians were all much impressed by the good manners of a simple herdsman.

"He is no simple herdsman," revealed Apollo. "He is a son of Priam. And my priest in Troy foretold that he would one day bring destruction to that city."

Thetis had been right when she had told Peleus that Zeus was planning a mighty war. Zeus had made up his mind that the populations both of Hellas and of the Asiatic side of the Hellespont must be reduced. To achieve this end, he intended to embroil Europe and Asia in war. Remembering the golden apple that Eris had rolled among the guests at Peleus's wedding, he decided to use it to stir up trouble. Hera, Athene, and Aphrodite had all expected to receive the apple from Peleus. Now Paris should decide who was the fairest of the three and award to her the golden apple. The three goddesses agreed to abide by the choice of the handsome young herdsman, and Paris, unwillingly, accepted the role of judge.

The goddesses argued for a while whether they should be judged clothed or unclothed. Athene was determined that Aphrodite should not wear her magic girdle, which made anybody she desired fall in love with her. Aphrodite for her part insisted that Athene should take off her helmet. So, in the end, it was agreed that all three should disrobe and appear naked in front of Paris.

Paris requested that each of the three goddesses should present herself before him in turn, out of sight and out of hearing of the others.

Hera, the Queen of Heaven, was the first. As Paris gazed in awe at her glorious figure, Hera told him that if he awarded her the golden apple she would make him the most powerful of all mortals and a ruler of many cities. Next came Athene, who promised him wisdom and victory in war. Lastly came Aphrodite, who promised him the most beautiful of mortal women—Helen.

"But she is the wife of King Menelaos of Sparta, the brother of the High King Agamemnon."

"I will take you to Sparta with my son Eros, and Helen will fall so passionately in love with you that she will follow you wherever you go."

Paris could not resist; he awarded the Apple of Discord to Aphrodite, and so made Hera and Athene his enemies.

How King Priam discovered that Paris was the son he believed was dead and how Paris went to Sparta and, with the help of Eros and Aphrodite, persuaded Helen to elope with him to Troy, must wait for another tale.

Menelaos appealed to his brother, King Agamemnon of Mycenae, for help. He wanted Agamemnon to lead an army against Troy to recover Helen and the treasure she had taken with her from Sparta.

The High King Agamemnon summoned all the kings and princes of Hellas to unite in assembling an army and a fleet to invade the Troad and bring back Helen to

Aphrodite, the fairest of them all

Menelaos. When Helen had chosen Menelaos to wed her, the many other suitors she had rejected had all sworn to stand behind Menelaos in future, and all of them declared their willingness to keep their vow. Kalchas, a renegade Trojan, much esteemed as an infallible prophet, now told Agamemnon that Troy could never be taken unless the young Achilles was with the invading fleet and army.

Agamemnon's chief adviser was Nestor, King of Pylos, the wisest of all the Greeks. He was now at least sixty years old but still able to fight. Nestor agreed to go to Iolkos and persuade Peleus to let his son join in the expedition. Nestor took with him Odysseus, the young King of Ithaka, whom he regarded as the heir to his wisdom. Nestor and Odysseus had no difficulty in persuading Peleus to let Achilles go. Peleus himself was now too old for active service.

Both Phoinix and Patrokles were delighted when Peleus agreed to let Achilles join the expedition with an army of Myrmidons and fifty ships. Peleus gave young Achilles the spear that had been Athene's wedding gift to him. He even gave him the two immortal horses that had been Poseidon's wedding present to him. One stipulation he did make: Achilles and his Myrmidons were not to be under the command of the High King Agamemnon.

At this time the Greek armies and ships were gathering at Aulis, where the island of Euboea is separated from the mainland of Hellas by no more than one hundred yards of sea. Helped by a northeast gale, Achilles reached Aulis safely with all his ships. But that same northeast gale prevented the Greek fleet from sailing against Troy.

Kalchas the seer told Agamemnon that the goddess Artemis was angry with him because he had killed one of her sacred hinds when out hunting. Kalchas went on to tell the High King that he could appease the anger of Artemis only by sacrificing his daughter Iphigeneia.

But Iphigeneia was in Mycenae. Agamemnon had to find an excuse for bringing her to Aulis. At the suggestion of Odysseus, he pretended that he wanted Iphigeneia to come to Aulis to marry the young Achilles.

When Achilles heard how his name had been used to deceive Iphigeneia, he was furious with Agamemnon. It was the beginning of a bitter hostility between Agamemnon and Achilles.

Achilles tried his utmost to save Iphigeneia from being sacrificed. He threatened to withdraw his Myrmidons and his ships from the expedition. He even declared his willingness to marry her. But Iphigeneia shook her head.

"No, no, I must die for the glory of Hellas."

And with these words she laid her head upon the block and awaited the sacrificial ax.

Suddenly there came a peal of thunder. The northeast gale instantly died away. The goddess Artemis came down, seized Iphigeneia and carried her off to become one of her priestesses at her temple in Tauris.

Just before the fleet sailed, Agamemnon was sacrificing to Zeus when a large serpent with blood-red spots over it

Peleus gave the two immortal horses

wriggled out from the altar and up into a plane tree, where a small bird had a nest and eight young ones. The serpent devoured all of them, then, as the mother-bird fluttered around, caught her in its jaws also. Then it coiled itself around the trunk of the tree. There was a flash of lightning and Zeus turned the serpent to stone. The seer Kalchas, called upon to interpret this strange incident, declared it meant that the war with Troy would last for nine years and that in the tenth year Troy would fall at last.

When the fleet sailed there was another violent storm. In the confusion the pilots lost their direction. Instead of landing in the Troad, they beached the ships in Mysia, which is the country south of Phrygia. The Mysians, finding themselves invaded by a strange army, fought back with determination and courage. Led by their King, Telephos, they drove the Greeks back to their ships. But Achilles and Patrokles quickly rallied the Greeks and put Telephos and his men to flight.

The Greeks had duly sacrificed to Dionysos before sailing, but the Mysians had for some time been neglecting the god of wine. To punish Telephos, Dionysos made a vine spring up in front of him as he ran. Telephos tripped, and was wounded in the thigh from a thrust by the invincible spear that Peleus had given to Achilles. The Greeks, anxious only to reach Troy, then left Mysia.

King Telephos's wound refused to heal and he went to consult the Oracle at Delphi. He was answered in the usual ambiguous style of the Oracle: "He that woundeth thee shall also heal thee." Telephos disguised himself as a beggar and went to Mycenae, where Agamemnon, after the muddle made of the first attempt to reach Troy, was busy reorganizing the Greek forces. Agamemnon had no desire to antagonize the Mysians, lest they decided to ally themselves to the Trojans. He asked Achilles to heal Telephos as the Oracle had foretold.

Achilles protested that any medicine he had ever been taught by Cheiron had long been forgotten. Odysseus, clever as usual, suggested that, as it was the spear that had wounded Telephos, some scrapings from it might heal the wound. This was a success, and Telephos went back to Mysia on good terms with the Greeks.

The Greek fleet now reached the small island of Tenedos, which is close to the Troad on the mainland. Here, under Agamemnon's orders, they waited for the return of Odysseus and Menelaos, who had gone to Troy with an ultimatum demanding the return of Helen and of the treasure she had taken from Sparta when she eloped with Paris. The ultimatum was refused.

Tenedos was ruled by a son of Apollo called Tenes. Before he had set out to join the expedition against Troy, Achilles had been warned by his mother that he must never kill a son of Apollo—because if he did Apollo would for ever afterward be his enemy and would ultimately ensure his death.

Tenes was furious when the Greek fleet came to Tenedos, and in order to show his enmity he went to the

A strange serpent appeared

top of a high cliff and hurled a great rock down on the Greek fleet. It fell close to one of the ships of the Myrmidons. In a rage Achilles jumped overboard and swam ashore. As soon as he came face to face with Tenes he thrust that deadly spear of his through Tenes's heart. Then he suddenly realized what he had done. He buried Tenes where he lay and was angered with Agamemnon for allowing the Greeks to land and ravage Tenedos.

The Greeks now sailed from Tenedos and beached their ships within sight of Troy. Achilles was on the point of leaping ashore when he remembered another of his mother's warnings. She had told him that the first Greek ashore in the Troad would inevitably be killed. So Achilles held back, and it was Protesilaos, a Thessalian prince, who was killed. For a time the Trojans managed to keep the Greeks from disembarking in force, but when Achilles landed he and his Myrmidons drove the Trojans back and the Greeks were able to land.

At that date siege warfare was completely undeveloped and the Greeks never supposed they would be able to conquer Troy by direct attack. All they could hope to do was to wear down Troy by isolating it and destroying its trade. The tale of the city's nine years of seige tends to be a monotonous list of battles in which the Olympians often played a part, Aphrodite and Apollo helping the Trojans, Hera, Athene, and Poseidon the Greeks.

By the beginning of the tenth year of the war, Troy was still impregnable, but the Trojans were feeling the strain on their resources through loss of trade. It was on one of the many expeditions to ravage the country around Troy, in the spring of the tenth year, when the great Trojan irises were in flower beside the river Scamander, that Chryseis, the daughter of Chryses, one of Apollo's priests, was awarded to Agamemnon as his share of the spoils. At the same time a beautiful girl called Briseis was allotted to Achilles.

Chryses was much upset by the capture of his beautiful daughter and offered Agamemnon a ransom for her return. Agamemnon had been much attracted by Chryseis and refused. So the priest prayed to Apollo to punish the Greeks. Apollo, who of all the Olympians was by now the bitterest enemy of the Greeks, at once answered his priest's appeal by sending a plague of dysentery into the Greek camp. Kalchas told Nestor and Odysseus why the plague had been sent and urged them to restore Chryseis to her father. For some time Agamemnon refused, but as the plague increased he unwillingly gave way. When Chryseis was given back to her father the plague immediately ceased.

Although Agamemnon was praised for his unselfish action, he still begrudged it and he was resentful that Achilles had been able to keep Briseis without any interference, human or divine. He had always been jealous of Achilles' renown as a warrior. So, now he seized Briseis.

Achilles, who was in love with Briseis, was furious with Agamemnon for this high-handed action.

Tenes challenged the Greek fleet

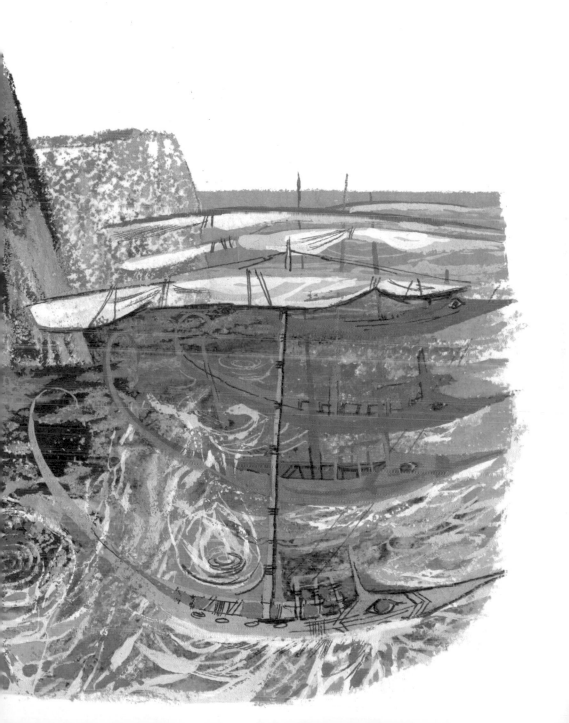

"I have had enough of that swollen-headed Achaean," he told Patrokles. "My Myrmidons and I are not Achaeans. Let them get on with the war as best they can without me. We fight no more to help them against Troy, and as soon as possible we shall return to Thessaly."

Patrokles was depressed to hear this. He was thoroughly enjoying himself in the war. However, when Achilles withdrew to his tent and ordered his Myrmidons to take no part in the fighting even if the Trojans tried to overrun the Greek camp, Patrokles remained silent. He knew how idle it would be to argue with Achilles in his present mood.

Without Achilles, the Greeks were soon hard beset by the Trojans. Ajax and Diomedes and Odysseus fought valiantly, but, under the leadership of Hektor, the noblest and most valiant of Priam's sons, the Trojans drove the Greeks back into their camp.

Realizing the danger, the leading Greek warriors implored Nestor to persuade Agamemnon to lay aside his pride and return Briseis to Achilles.

Nestor managed to convince Agamemnon that the war would end disastrously for the Greeks unless Achilles could be induced to fight again.

It must be admitted that when Agamemnon decided to apologize to Achilles he apologized handsomely. An embassy consisting of Odysseus and Phoinix, the old tutor of Achilles, whom he loved and respected, offered on behalf of Agamemnon to restore Briseis and pay a large sum of gold. If the war against Troy should end in victory for the Greeks, Agamemnon offered Achilles any one of his three daughters in marriage, and seven cities as her dowry.

Odysseus raised every argument he could think of to persuade Achilles to accept this magnificent offer, but Achilles sat in silent gloom. Then old Phoinix did his utmost by talking about the days when Peleus took his son away from Skyros to dress him as a boy again.

"Would your old tutor give you bad advice, my son? Remember that it was I who persuaded your noble father to let you leave for Aulis with fifty ships. Remember that it was I who persuaded him to give you his suit of golden armor, his wedding present from the Olympians, and the deadly spear given him by the goddess Athene, and even the two immortal horses given by Poseidon. Listen to me, do listen to me, my son, and harness those horses to your chariot and wield again that deadly spear."

But Achilles sat obstinately silent.

The continued absence of Achilles from the battlefield around Troy made the Trojans bolder and bolder. At last, they made a full-scale assault on the Greek camp.

The Greeks had taken advantage of an armistice to build a wall behind the trench that defended their encampment. To their consternation the wall was breached, and to their still greater dismay a torch flung by Hektor set fire to the first ship the Greeks had beached ten years ago, the ship of Protesilaos.

Even Achilles was shaken for a moment.

The ship of Protesilaos was set on fire

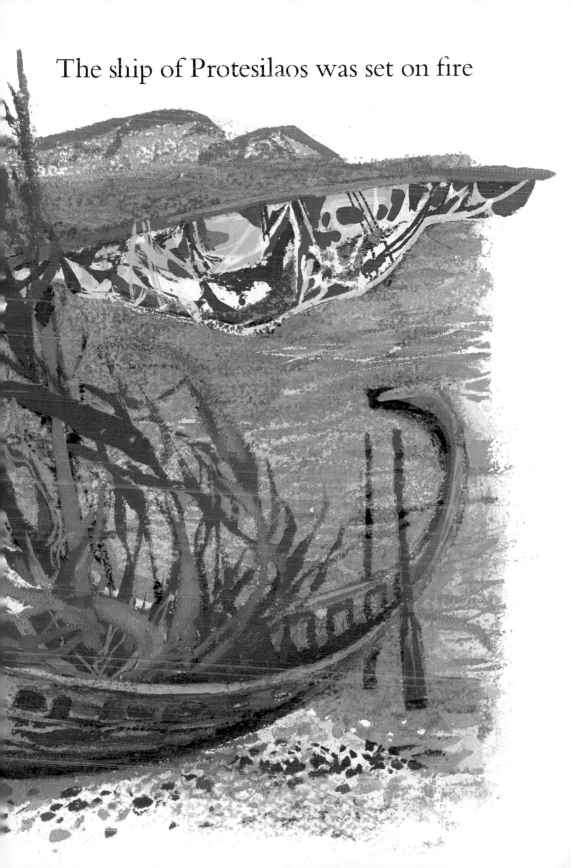

"No matter," he said to Patrokles. "Provided our own ships are not fired we shall be sailing back to Thessaly in a day or two."

However, Patrokles continued to argue with him.

"Suppose they do succeed in firing our ships, how shall we ever reach Thessaly? I beg you to let me lead your Myrmidons into the fight. Let me wear your golden armor and the Trojans, thinking it is you fighting them, will draw back."

Achilles still hesitated.

"I beg you to listen to me," Patrokles urged. "I beg you to let me drive the Trojans back from our encampment, and save the ships from being burned."

Achilles could not help being moved by what was almost agony in the voice of his dearest friend.

"So be it," he said at last.

So Patrokles put on the golden armor. But when he armed himself with his friend's deadly spear, Achilles said, in a voice that Patrokles knew he must not argue with, "No, no, the armor is enough. You might lose my spear in battle. Moreover, Athene might be offended if I lent the spear she gave my father to anyone else. With Apollo so active on behalf of the Trojans we need all the help that Athene and great Hera can give us."

So Patrokles, wearing the golden armor and rallying the Myrmidons, attacked the Trojans. They supposed that he was the invincible Achilles himself, and retreated in confusion. In the exhilaration of his success, Patrokles reached the very walls of Troy. He even wondered whether it was to fall to him to lead the Greeks in a final victorious assault upon the city that had withstood ten long years of siege. Then, suddenly, he found himself facing a gleaming shield. Behind the shield was Apollo himself. Always active on behalf of the Trojans, the god feared that Patrokles might indeed inspire the Greeks to scale the walls of Troy in sufficient numbers to overcome the garrison. It is possible that Apollo mistook Patrokles for Achilles. At any rate, he cast a mist over him and buffeted him so severely that Patrokles was so dazed he hardly knew if he was still standing on his feet. At that moment the great Hektor, who had been fighting hard to rally the Trojans, encountered Patrokles and, after a short duel, killed him and stripped the armor from his corpse.

There was now a desperate struggle for the body of Patrokles, which many of the Trojans still thought to be the body of Achilles.

When the news of Patrokles' death was brought to Achilles, he rushed unarmed from his tent in a frenzy of grief. The sound of his war cry ringing out after so long a silence had such an effect on the Trojans that the Greeks were able to recover Patrokles' body.

When he saw the corpse of his beloved friend, Achilles threw himself down beside it, and in paroxysms of grief mourned for his lost companion of so many years.

"And it was I who killed him," he sobbed. "Why did I consent to lend him my armor? Why did I mind whether

Patrokles rode into battle

the Trojans fired our ships or not? O Patrokles, my beloved Patrokles, where are you now?"

Suddenly he leaped up and, without armor, rushed toward the battle. Odysseus managed to restrain him and persuaded him to hold back until Hephaistos could forge for him a new suit of armor.

Achilles agreed to wait for the armor, which was to be brought to him next day, but he was determined to meet and kill Hektor before the funeral of Patrokles.

When, on the following day, Achilles appeared duly armed, such was the fury of his attack that the Trojans broke into three groups, the larger body quickly retreating across the plain toward the city walls. Achilles drove the rest of the Trojan forces into a bend of the river Scamander. Here they would all have perished if Achilles had not been so intent on coming face to face with Hektor. The noblest of the sons of Priam had been badly bruised by a large stone flung at him by Ajax during the fight for the body of Patrokles. However, he felt that, at whatever cost to himself, he could not seem to be afraid to answer the challenge of Achilles to single combat. So, though feeling far from fit to meet the most formidable of all the Greeks, Hektor decided he must accept the challenge. When he came out from the city gates, Greeks and Trojans drew back to watch this mortal combat between the two greatest warriors of the small world of long ago.

Hektor, realizing how seriously that blow from a stone had handicapped him, thought of a way in which he in his turn could handicap his opponent. For weeks now, Achilles had been sitting in his tent without taking any exercise, let alone fighting. He was probably already rather short of breath. If he could be made still more breathless, then Hektor might be able to hold out against him until sundown. Then the combat would have to be resumed next day, by which time Hektor might have recovered his strength.

So, to the amazement of all those who had lowered their arms to watch, Hektor began to run away around the city walls. Twice around the city walls Achilles pursued him; but, alas for Hektor's hopes, when he turned and stood to face Achilles the latter was not in the least breathless. He did not wait to draw his sword but drove his deadly spear into Hektor's breast.

As the noblest of Priam's sons lay dying, he gasped an appeal to Achilles to allow his body to be ransomed for burial. Achilles grimly shook his head.

"You killed my dearest friend," he said, "and for that your body shall rot unburied."

From brutal speech Achilles went on to much more brutal action. He stripped the armor from the dead body of the once mighty Hektor, and sent it back to the Greek encampment. Then he slit through the flesh behind the tendons of Hektor's heels and with leather thongs fastened them to his chariot. When the body was firmly secured, Achilles got into his chariot and, whipping up its three white horses, drove three times around the walls of Troy.

Hektor's body dragged around the walls

It was an agonizing sight for Hektor's devoted wife Andromache to see that body she had loved so deeply being dragged along in a cloud of dust. When Achilles had exulted sufficiently in the piteous sight he was offering to the people of Troy, he drove slowly back to the Greek encampment. There he left the body of Hektor lying unattended under the hot sun while he began the preparations for the funeral of Patrokles.

Warriors were sent off to gather timber, and the largest funeral pyre ever raised was built to cremate the corpse of Patrokles. Cattle were sacrificed, and two of the hounds from the pack of nine with which Patrokles had hunted. Achilles, still indulging in what was beginning to seem unreasonable grief for his dead friend, was on the point of throwing the body of Hektor to the seven remaining hounds when Aphrodite restrained him.

"You have already incurred my ill will by attacking my son Aeneas and driving away his flocks from Mount Ida. Beware, Achilles, of my enmity."

Achilles refrained from throwing the corpse of Hektor to the pack, but after the funeral games were over he continued to indulge his grief by rising every day at dawn to lash the corpse of Hektor to his chariot and drag it three times around the funeral pyre of Patrokles. Apollo, now more than ever an enemy of Achilles, preserved the body from being corrupted.

Thetis now appealed to Father Zeus himself to make it possible for her to offer the body of Hektor for ransom.

She was dreading the hostility of Apollo and Aphrodite and hoped to prevent Achilles from giving them any further offence. Zeus listened to her plea and sent Hermes to escort King Priam one night to where Achilles lay fast asleep in his tent. Hermes woke Achilles and advised him to grant Priam's request to ransom the body of his son so that it might be given burial. He added that Achilles should realize that Priam might easily have strangled him while he was sleeping so heavily. The messenger of the Olympians vanished, leaving Priam and Achilles to talk alone. Achilles agreed to Priam's request to ransom Hektor's body.

"What ransom do you demand?" Priam asked.

"A weight of gold equal to the body of your son," Achilles replied.

Priam accepted the terms, although he knew that his treasury, already depleted by the heavy financial strain of the war, would be almost emptied by this untoward further strain.

Achilles set up a huge pair of scales under the city walls. In one scale-pan the body of Hektor was placed; into the other were placed ingots of gold. From the city walls the Trojans looked down in anguish, because in spite of all the gold the weight of Hektor's body still kept the scale-pan with the gold aloft.

At last, when only a few inches were needed to raise the body to the same weight as the gold, Polyxena, the most beautiful of Priam's daughters, threw down from the

Hektor's body outweighed the gold

wall all her own bracelets and necklaces. They turned the scale, and a great shout of relief went up from the anxious spectators on the city walls; the body of the noblest Trojan would now be buried, with much public lamentation, among his own people.

Achilles was filled with admiration as he watched the Princess Polyxena giving away her own golden bracelets and necklaces to secure the body of her beloved brother. He saw Andromache embracing Polyxena with tears of gratitude, and in that moment fell passionately in love with the Trojan Princess. He told Priam that if he would give Polyxena to him in wedlock she should be the ransom for Hektor. Moreover, if Priam would persuade Paris to give Helen back to Menelaos he would use all his influence and do everything in his power to promote a lasting peace between Hellas and Troy.

Priam replied that for the present he was content to ransom Hektor's body with gold, but he added that if Achilles could persuade the Greeks to depart without Helen he would certainly be willing to grant him Polyxena's hand in marriage.

Achilles agreed to do what he could.

"Polyxena is the only woman I have desired in wedlock," he declared.

Priam then took the body of Hektor for burial.

Notwithstanding the strain upon the Trojan resources, the diminishing treasury, and the loss of trade, King Priam still had faithful allies. Some years before,

Penthesileia, the Queen of the Amazons, had accidentally killed her sister Hippolyta with an ill-aimed arrow while they were hunting. This had been a great anguish to Penthesileia and she had come to the court of King Priam for him to absolve her of the death of her beloved sister.

Now, to repay Priam for his kindness, she brought her Amazons from their country on the northern shore of the Pontus Euxinus, which we call the Black Sea.

Queen Penthesileia and her Amazons fought with such skill and courage that they did serious damage to the Greek forces. Penthesileia was a daughter of Ares, the god of war, and as formidable as she was beautiful. On two or three occasions, she compelled Achilles himself to retreat, but in the end he killed her. As she lay dying, Achilles, overwhelmed with remorse, took her in his arms and kissed her lips. Then he buried Penthesileia with his own hands and mourned for her.

Thetis knew that her son's death was now near at hand and in an attempt to propitiate Apollo she advised Achilles to go to Lesbos, where he offered sacrifices to Apollo, Artemis, and their mother Leto.

Back in the Troad, the Trojans, with the help of Memnon, the black King of Ethiopia, who had come from the farthest south of that small world of long ago, nearly succeeded in burning the Greek ships. They were driven back when Achilles returned and killed Memnon.

It was to be the last achievement of Achilles. While the battle raged by one of the gates of the impregnable city,

Ajax carried Achilles from the battlefield

Apollo bade Paris shoot a poisoned arrow at Achilles and he directed that arrow to pierce Achilles in his right heel, his only vulnerable spot. It was poetic justice that Achilles, who had dragged Hektor by the heels three times around the city, should now die from a poisoned heel. There was a terrific fight for the corpse of Achilles but at last Ajax threw it over his shoulders and through a shower of arrows brought it back to the Greek camp.

Here for seventeen days Thetis and the Nereids mourned for Achilles, while the nine Muses chanted dirges. Thetis then went to Olympus to plead with Zeus to bestow immortality upon her son. Zeus, never able to resist a plea from Thetis, granted her request. While the funeral games were still in progress, Thetis descended from Olympus and took from the blazing fire the soul of Achilles. The home she chose for that soul was a little wooded island called Louke, which was close to the mouth of the Danube. Here for many years to come Achilles would be revered as a demi-god.

There is no space to tell here of the fall of Troy and of the wooden horse within which the Greeks passed through the gates of the city. But a word must be said about the end of Paris. He, too, was struck by a poisoned arrow. In his agony he managed to reach Mount Ida, where his happy youth had been spent, and to find Oenone, whom he had deserted to go in search of Helen. Oenone refused to give him herbs to soothe his pain, but when he died she was so unhappy that she killed herself.

The Travels of Achilles

HELLAS

THESSALY

MOUNT PELION
Iolkos

Delphi

Aulis

EUBOEA

AEGEAN SEA

SKYROS

Mycenae

Sparta

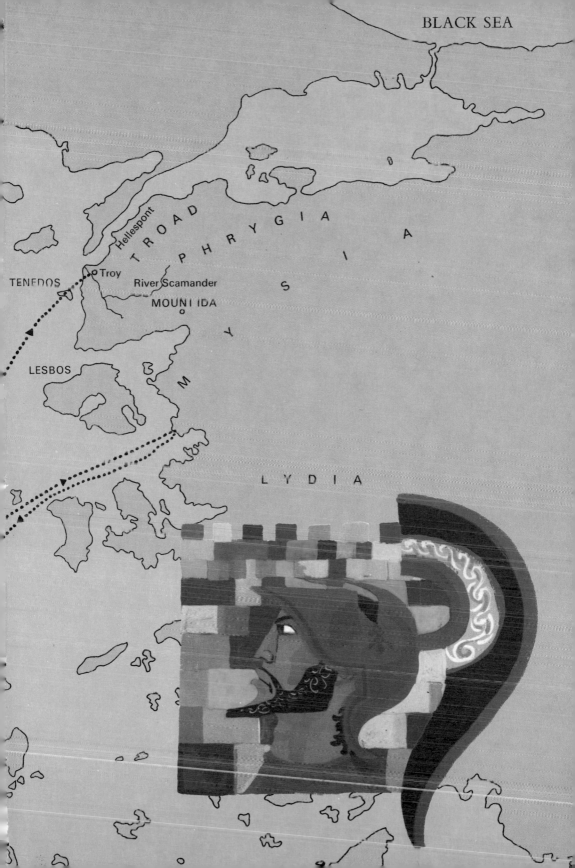

BLACK SEA

TENEDOS

TROAD

Hellespont

Troy

River Scamander

MOUNT IDA

LESBOS

PHRYGIA

MYSIA

LYDIA